EASY PIANO EDITION

GREAT PIANO SOLOS

CW00644644

Published by
Wise Publications
14-15 Berners Street, London W1T 3LJ, UK.

Exclusive Distributors:
Music Sales Limited
Distribution Centre, Newmarket Road, Bury St Edmunds, Suffolk IP33 3YB, UK.
Music Sales Pty Limited
20 Resolution Drive, Caringbah, NSW 2229, Australia.

Order No. AM993520
ISBN: 978-1-84772-543-1
This book © Copyright 2008 Wise Publications,
a division of Music Sales Limited.

Unauthorised reproduction of any part of this publication by
any means including photocopying is an infringement of copyright.

Edited by Jenni Wheeler.
Arranged and engraved by Camden Music.

Cover image based on original sculpture,
The Horn of Africa, 2006 by Michael Parekowhai
Courtesy of the artist and Roslyn Oxley9 Gallery
Cover designed by Liz Barrand.

Printed in the EU.

Your Guarantee of Quality
As publishers, we strive to produce every book to the highest commercial standards.
This book has been carefully designed to minimise awkward page turns and to make playing from it a real pleasure.
Particular care has been given to specifying acid-free, neutral-sized paper made from
pulps which have not been elemental chlorine bleached.
This pulp is from farmed sustainable forests and was produced with special regard for the environment.
Throughout, the printing and binding have been planned to ensure a sturdy,
attractive publication which should give years of enjoyment.
If your copy fails to meet our high standards, please inform us and we will gladly replace it.

www.musicsales.com

EASY PIANO EDITION

GREAT PIANO SOLOS

WISE PUBLICATIONS
part of The Music Sales Group
London / New York / Paris / Sydney / Copenhagen / Berlin / Madrid / Tokyo

CLASSICAL MUSIC

FILM THEMES

GREAT STANDARDS

Adagio For Strings

Music by Samuel Barber

Molto adagio ♩ = c.42

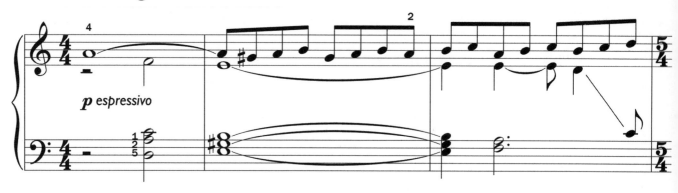

p espressivo

© Copyright 1939 (Renewed) by G. Schirmer Inc. (ASCAP).
This arrangement © Copyright 2006 by G. Schirmer, Inc. (ASCAP).
All Rights Reserved. International Copyright Secured. Used by Permission.

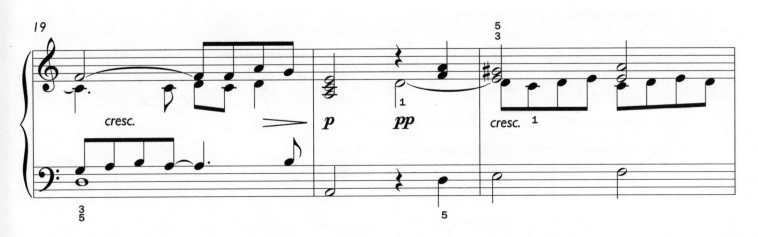

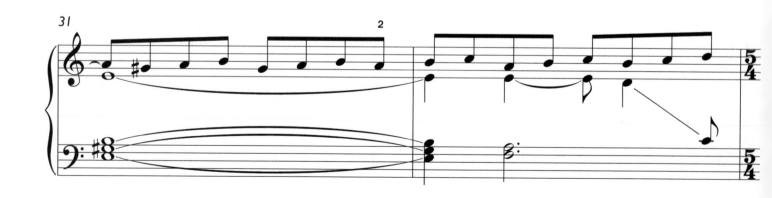

Canon in D

Composed by Johann Pachelbel

© Copyright 2008 Dorsey Brothers Music Limited.
All Rights Reserved. International Copyright Secured.

11

Eine Kleine Nachtmusik, K525

(1st Movement: Allegro)

Composed by Wolfgang Amadeus Mozart

Allegro ♩= 128

© Copyright 2008 Dorsey Brothers Music Limited.
All Rights Reserved. International Copyright Secured.

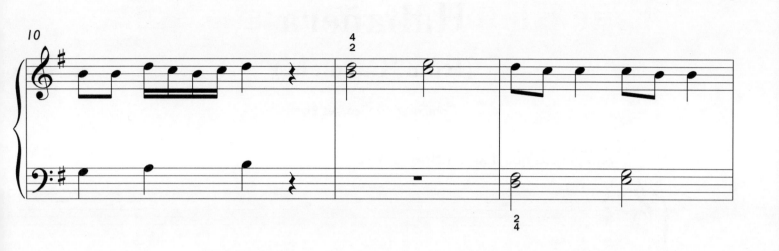

Habañera
(from 'Carmen')

Composed by Georges Bizet

Allegretto quasi andantino ♩ = 72

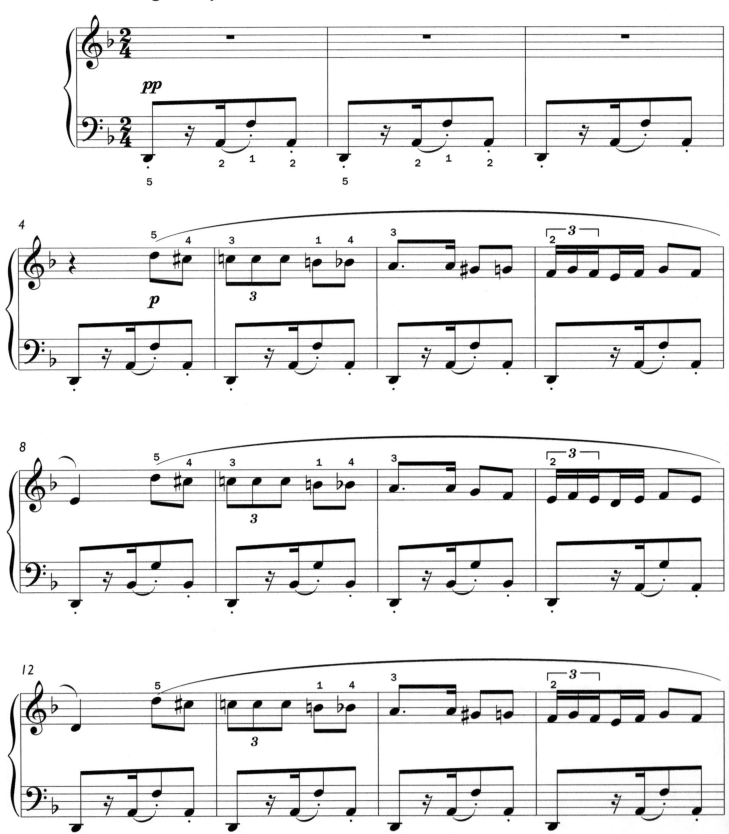

© Copyright 2008 Dorsey Brothers Music Limited.
All Rights Reserved. International Copyright Secured.

Sarabande in D minor

Music by George Frideric Handel

© Copyright 2008 Dorsey Brothers Music Limited.
All Rights Reserved. International Copyright Secured.

The English Patient

Music by Gabriel Yared

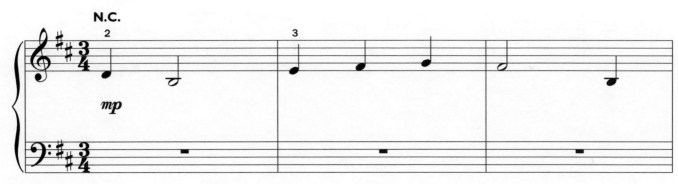

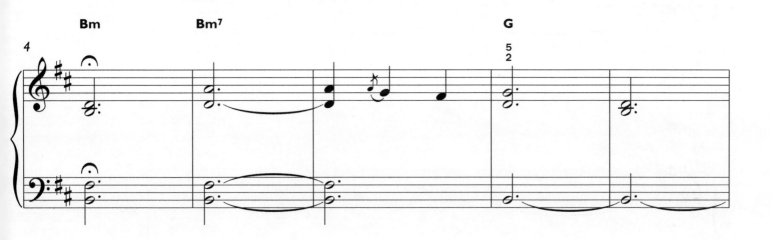

© Copyright 1997 English Patient Music.
Prestige Music Limited.
All Rights Reserved. International Copyright Secured.

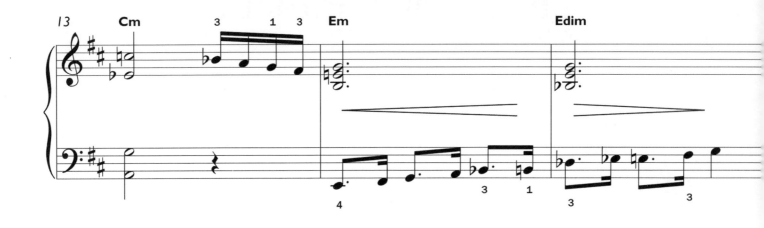

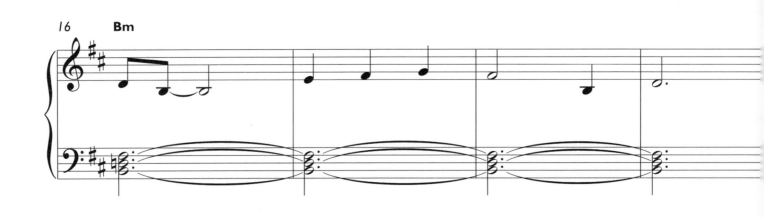

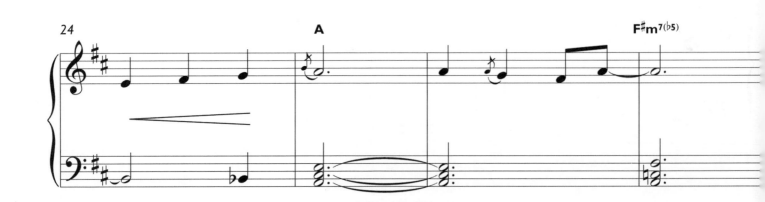

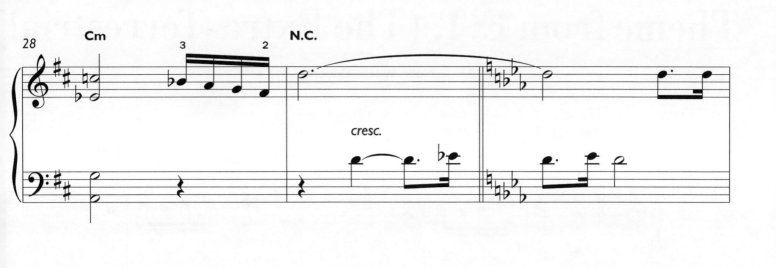

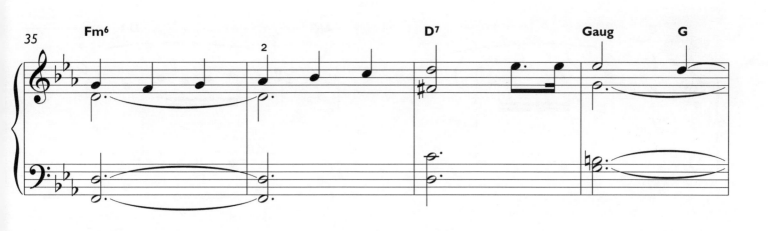

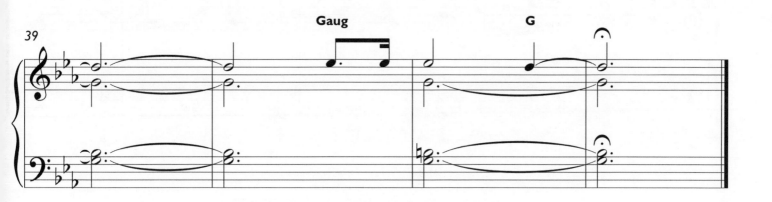

Theme from E.T. (The Extra-Terrestrial)

Music by John Williams

© Copyright 1982 Music Corporation of America Incorporated, USA.
Universal/MCA Music Limited.
All rights in Germany administered by Universal/MCA Music Publ. GmbH.
All Rights Reserved. International Copyright Secured.

Feather Theme
(Main Title from the film 'Forrest Gump')

Music by Alan Silvestri

Sweetly ♩ = 104

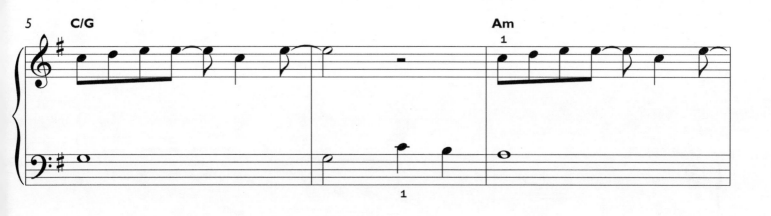

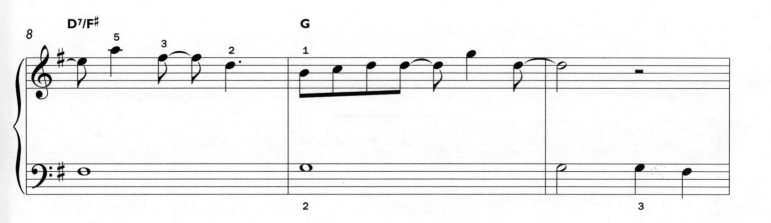

© Copyright 1994 Ensign Music Corporation/Famous Music Corporation, USA.
All Rights Reserved. International Copyright Secured.

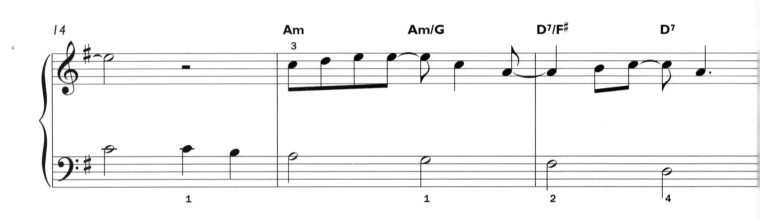

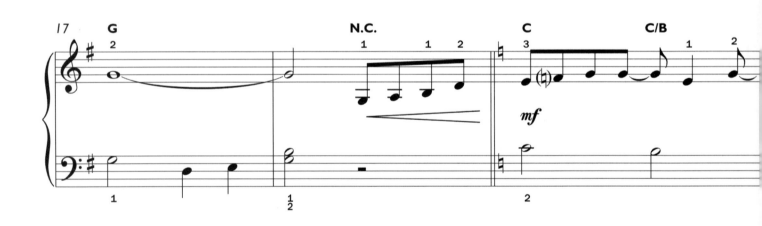

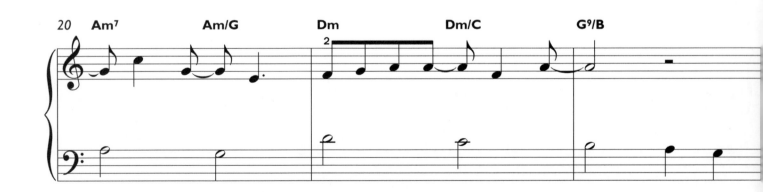

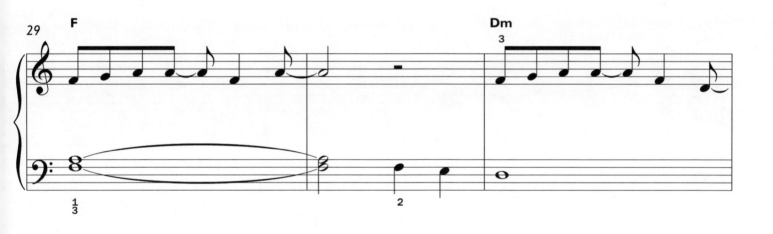

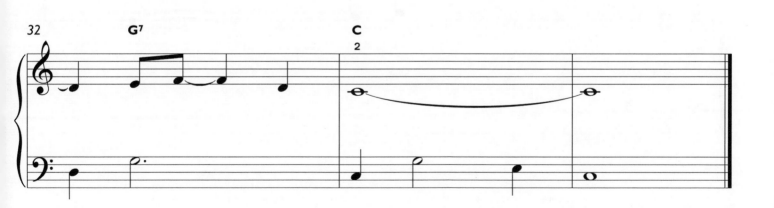

Into The West

(from 'The Lord Of The Rings: The Return Of The King')

Words & Music by Annie Lennox, Howard Shore & Fran Walsh

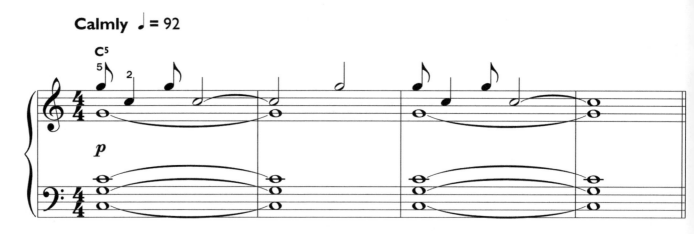

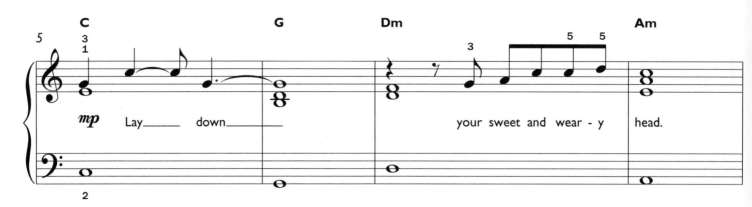

Lay___ down___ — your sweet and wear - y head.

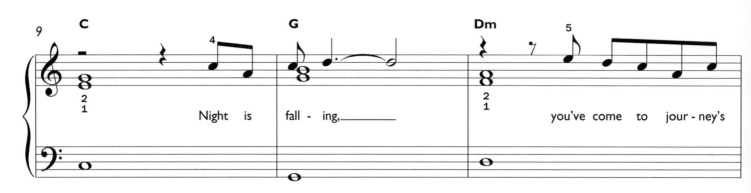

Night is fall - ing,___ you've come to jour - ney's

end. Sleep___ now,___ and

© Copyright 2003 La Lennoxa Music Company Limited/South Fifth Avenue Publishing/New Line Tunes, USA.
Warner/Chappell Music Limited (58.34%)/Universal Music Publishing MGB Limited (33.33%)/Sony/ATV Music Publishing (UK) Limited(8.33%).
All Rights in Germany Administered by Musik Edition Discoton GmbH (A Division of Universal Music Publishing Group).
All Rights Reserved. International Copyright Secured.

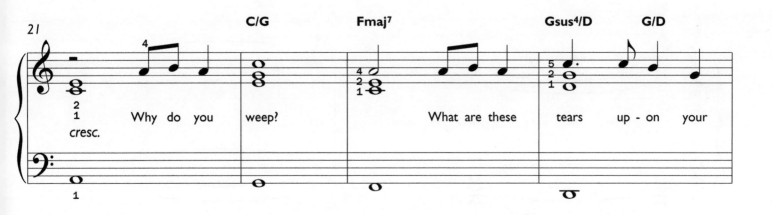

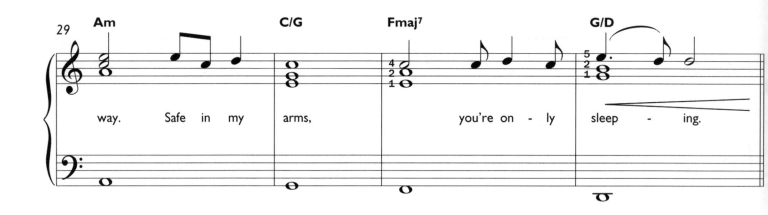

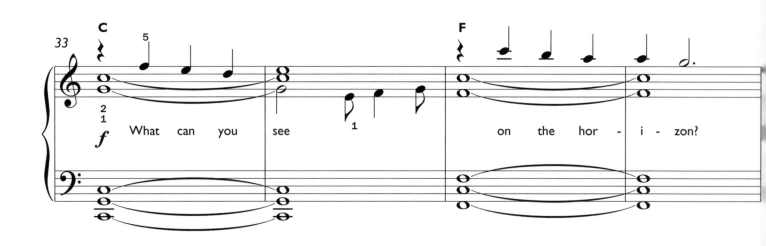

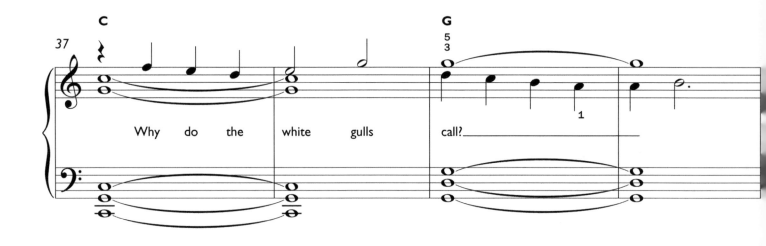

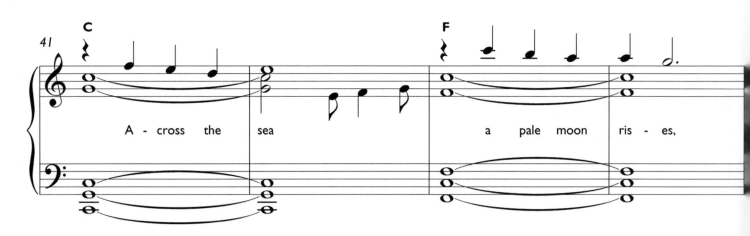

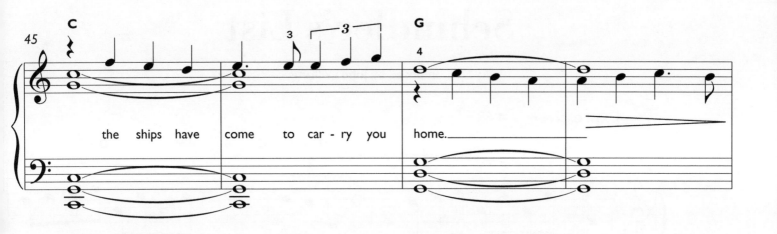

the ships have come to car - ry you home.

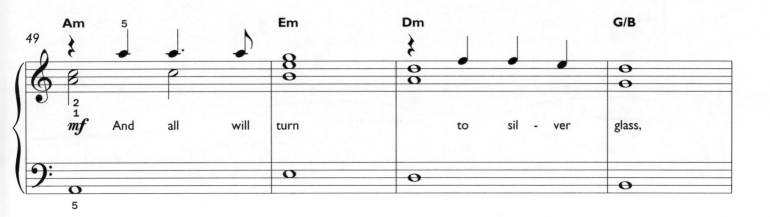

mf And all will turn to sil - ver glass,

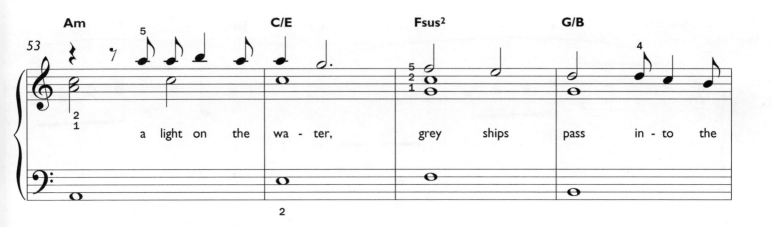

a light on the wa - ter, grey ships pass in - to the

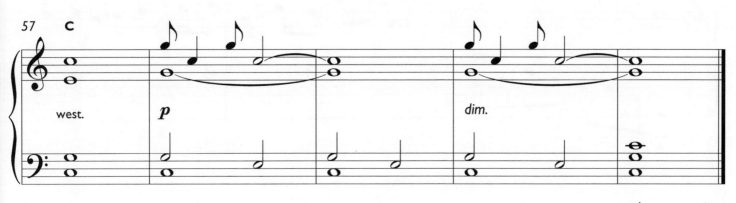

west.   *p*   *dim.*

8vb - - - - - - - - |

29

Schindler's List

Composed by John Williams

© Copyright 1993 Music Corporation of America Incorporated, USA.
Universal/MCA Music Limited.
All rights in Germany administered by Universal/MCA Music Publ. GmbH.
All Rights Reserved. International Copyright Secured.

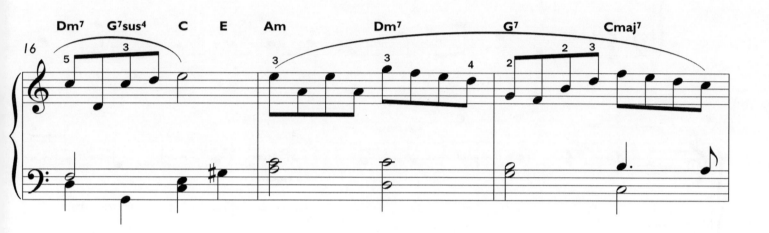

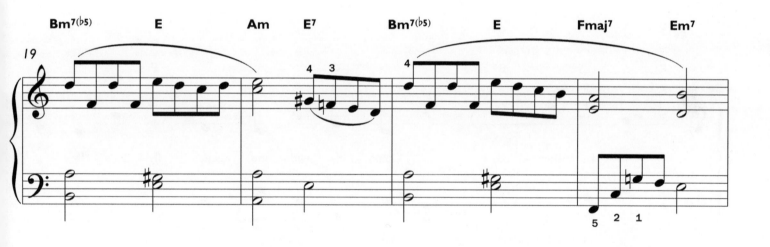

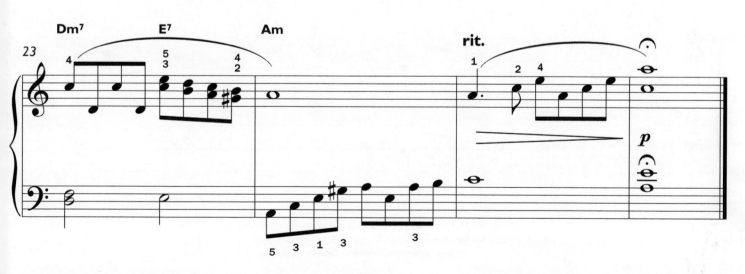

Come Fly With Me

Words by Sammy Cahn & Music by Jimmy Van Heusen

© Copyright 1958 Maraville Music Corporation, USA/Cahn Music Company, USA.
Chelsea Music Publishing Company Limited (50%)/Warner/Chappell North America Limited (50%).
All Rights Reserved. International Copyright Secured.

33

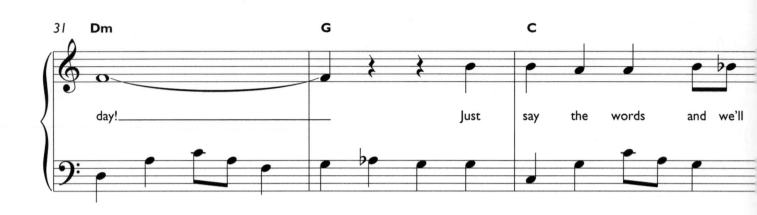

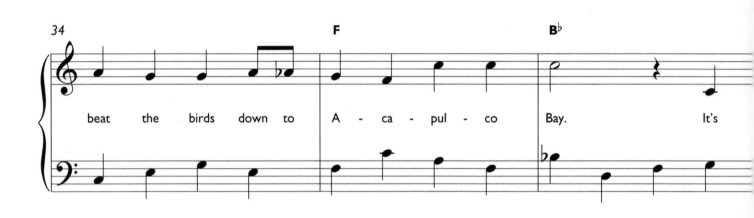

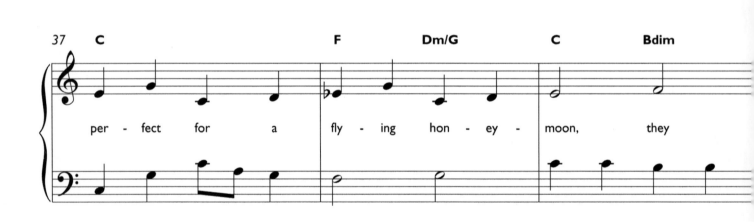

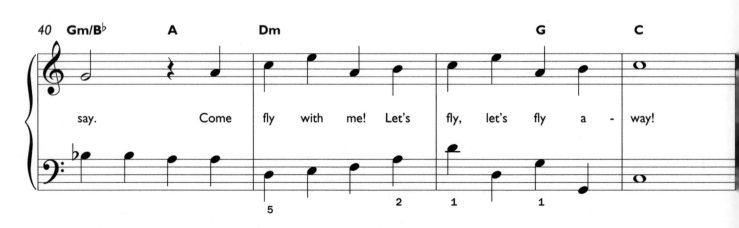

Mona Lisa

Words & Music by Jay Livingston & Ray Evans

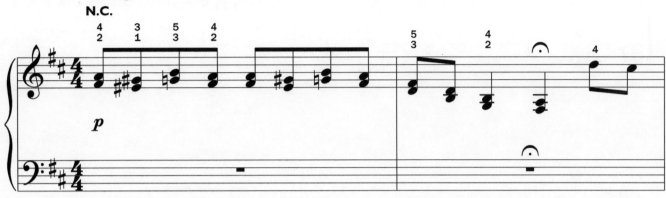

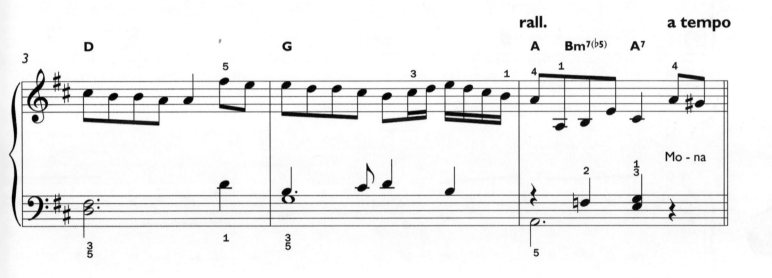

© Copyright 1949 Famous Music Corporation, USA.
All Rights Reserved. International Copyright Secured.

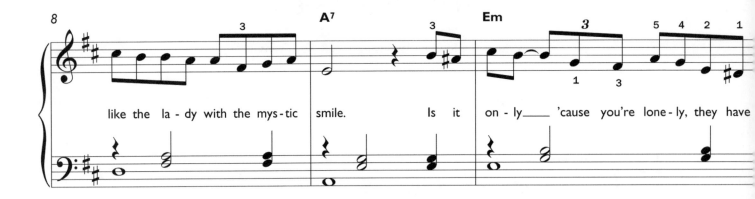

like the la - dy with the mys - tic smile. Is it on - ly____ 'cause you're lone - ly, they have

blamed you for that Mo - na Li - sa strange - ness in your smile? Do you

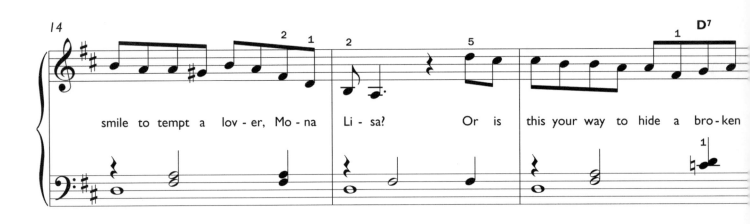

smile to tempt a lov - er, Mo - na Li - sa? Or is this your way to hide a bro - ken

heart? Man - y dreams have been brought to your door - step, they just

37

Pennies From Heaven

Words by Johnny Burke & Music by Arthur Johnston

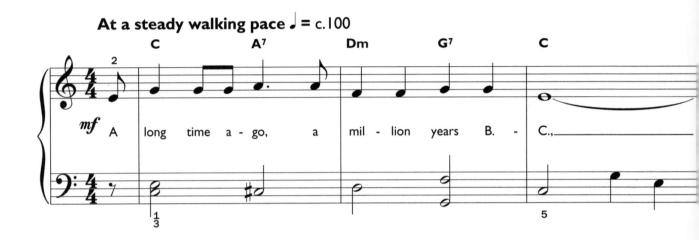

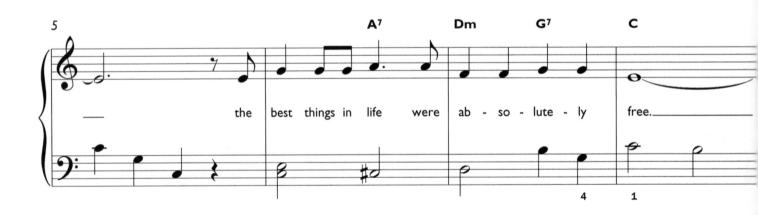

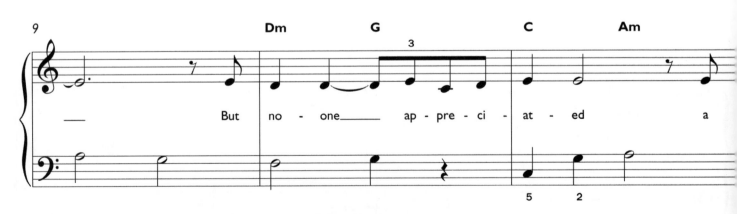

© Copyright 1936 Santly-Joy Incorporated, USA.
Campbell Connelly & Company Limited.
All Rights Reserved. International Copyright Secured.

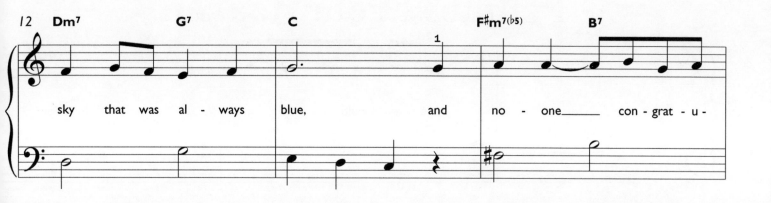

sky that was al - ways blue, and no - one____ con - grat - u -

-la - ted a moon that was al - ways new. So it was

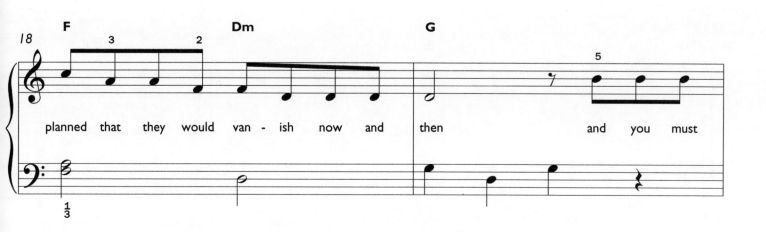

planned that they would van - ish now and then and you must

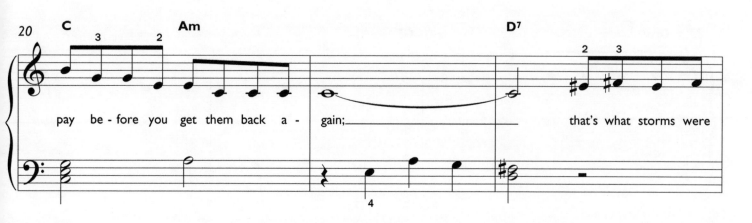

pay be - fore you get them back a - gain;____ that's what storms were

made for, and you should-n't be a - fraid... For

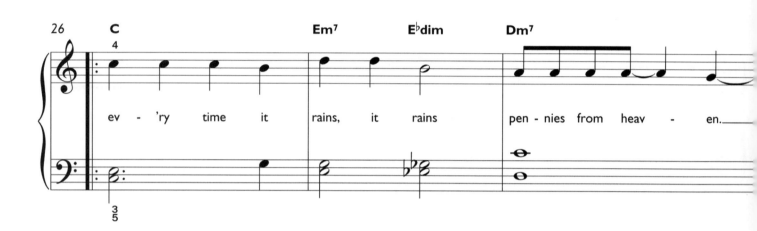

ev - 'ry time it rains, it rains pen - nies from heav - en.___

Don't you know each cloud con - tains

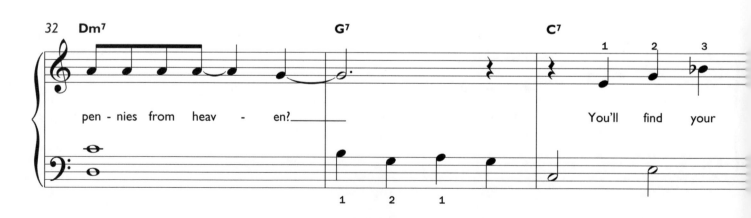

pen - nies from heav - en?___ You'll find your

fortune fall - ing   all o - ver   town.   Be sure that

your um - brel - la   is up - side   down.   Trade them for a

pack - age of   sun - shine and flow - ers.

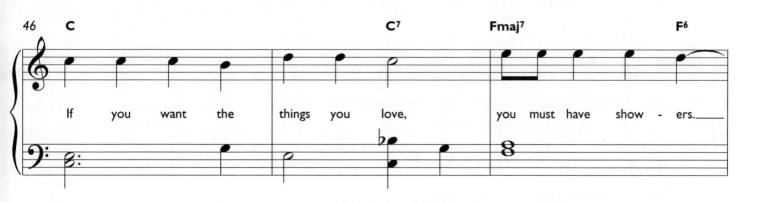

If you want the   things you love,   you must have show - ers.

So when you hear it thun - der

I.

don't run un - der a tree, there'll be pen - nies from heav - en for

2.

you and me. For tree, there'll be

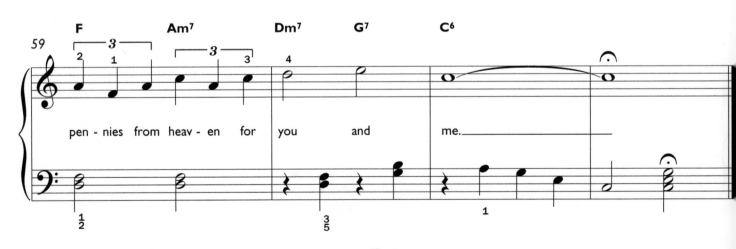

pen - nies from heav - en for you and me.

Strangers In The Night

Words by Charles Singleton & Eddie Snyder
Music by Bert Kaempfert

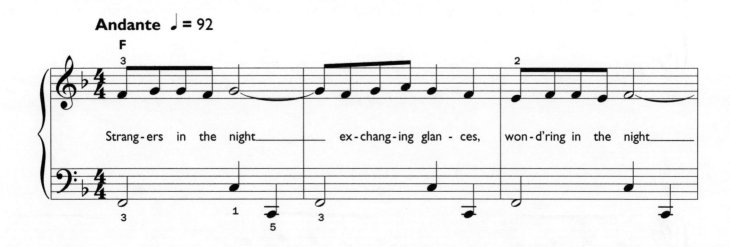

© Copyright 1966 Champion Music Corporation/Screen Gems-EMI Music Limited.
Universal/MCA Music Limited.
All rights in Germany administered by Universal/MCA Music Publ. GmbH.
All Rights Reserved. International Copyright Secured.

was so in-vit-ing, some-thing in your smile____ was so ex-cit-ing,

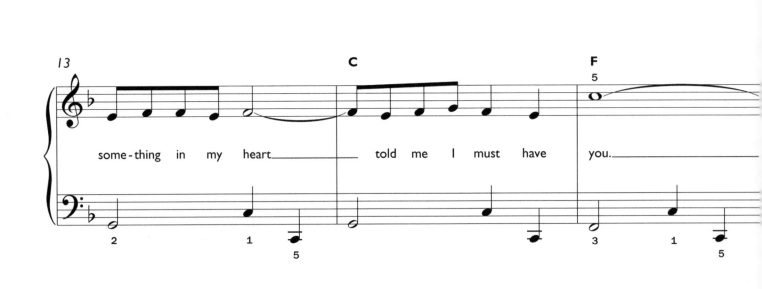

some-thing in my heart____ told me I must have you.____

Strang-ers in the night,____ two lone-ly peo-ple, we were

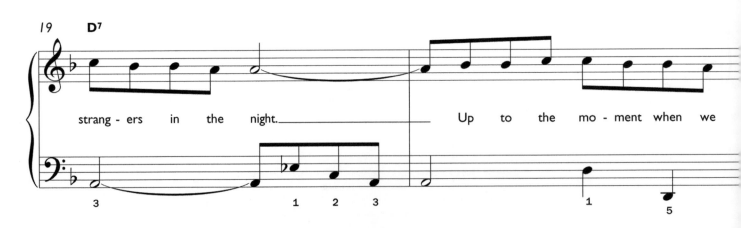

strang-ers in the night.____ Up to the mo-ment when we

said our first hel - lo,   lit - tle did we know   love was just a glance a - way, a

warm em - brac - ing dance a - way. And   ev - er since that night,_____

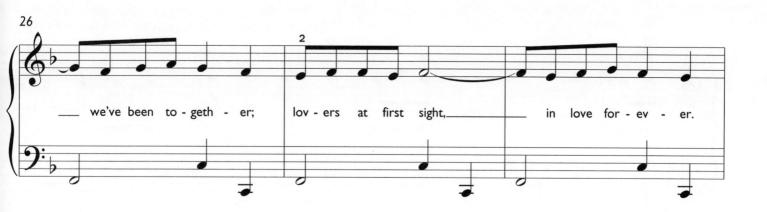

_____ we've been to - geth - er;   lov - ers at first sight,_____   in love for - ev - er.

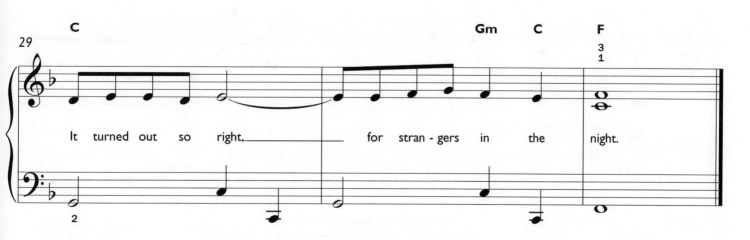

It turned out so right,_____   for stran - gers in the   night.

The Very Thought Of You

Words & Music by Ray Noble

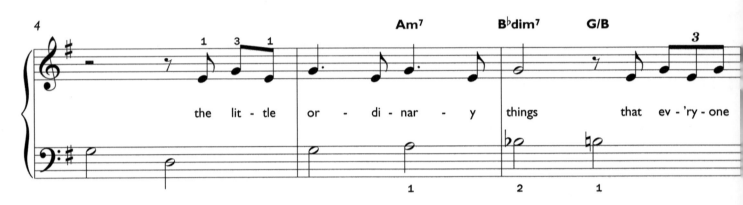

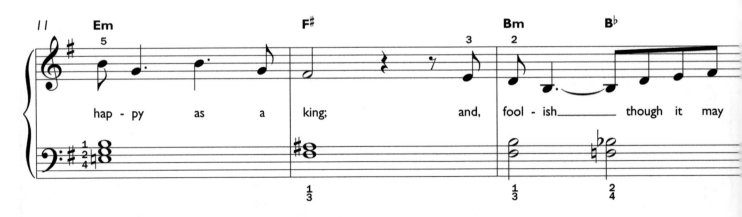

© Copyright 1934 Redwood Music Limited.

All Rights Reserved. International Copyright Secured.

Desafinado (Slightly Out Of Tune)

Words by Newton Mendonca & Music by Antonio Carlos Jobim

Medium Bossa Nova ♩ = 132

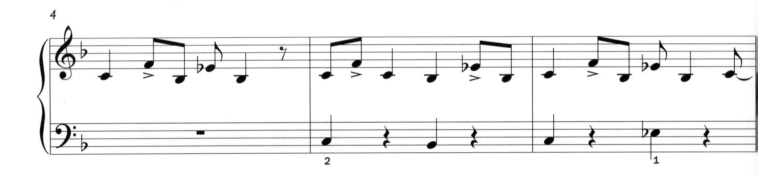

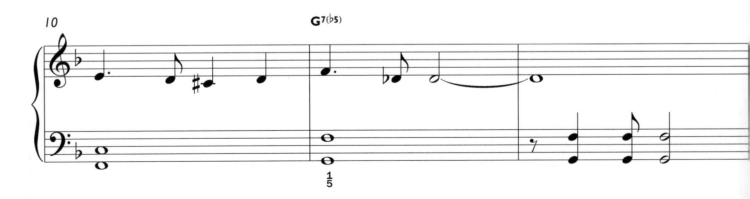

© Copyright 1959 Fermata do Brasil/IMG Songs UK.
All Rights Reserved. International Copyright Secured.

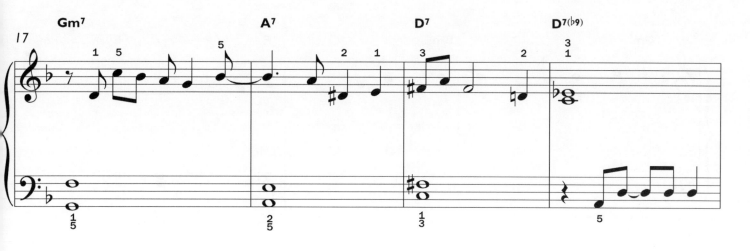

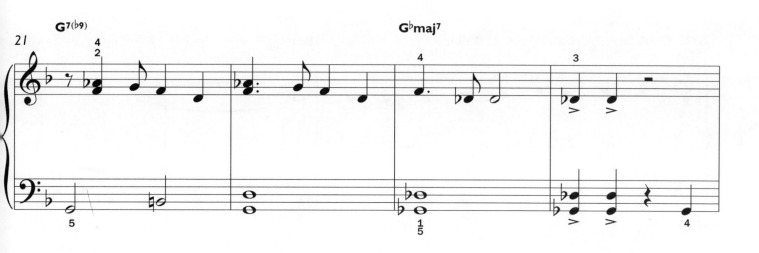

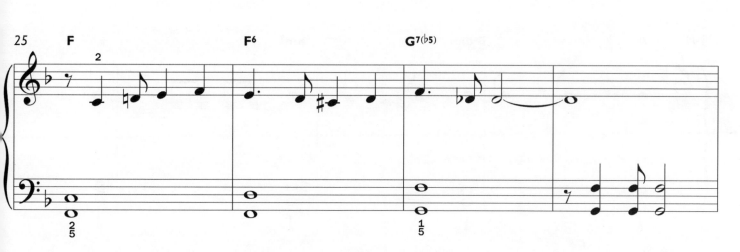

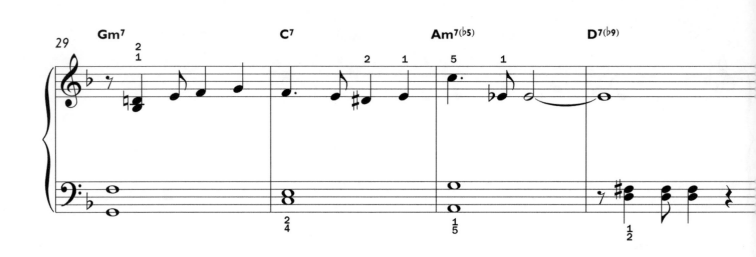

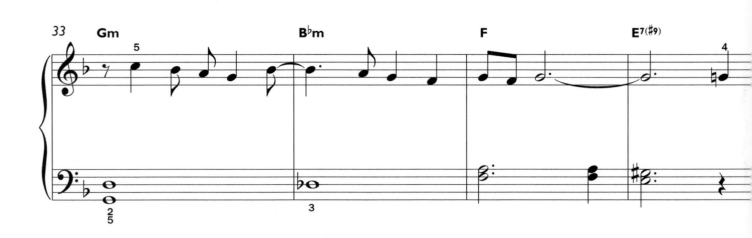

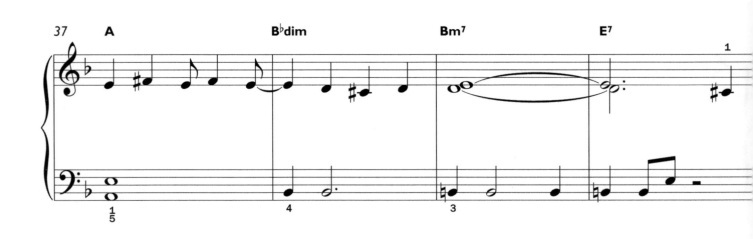

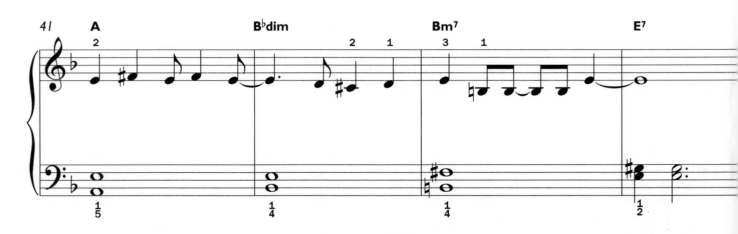

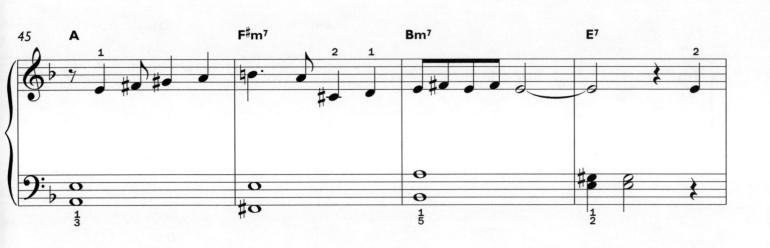

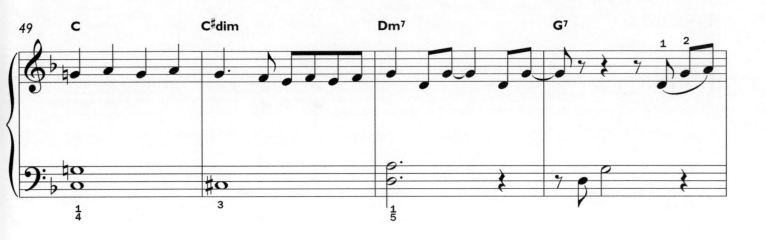

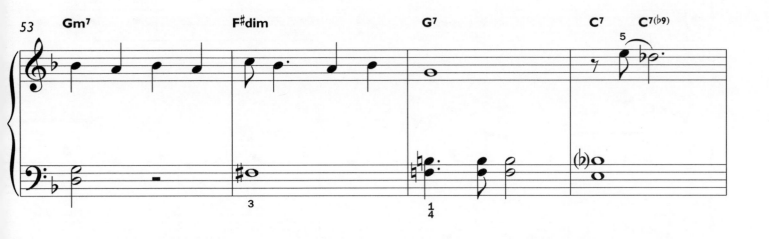

Wish I Knew How It Would Feel To Be Free

Words by Billy Taylor & Dick Dallas
Music by Billy Taylor

© Copyright 1964 & 1968 Duane Music Incorporated, USA.
Westminster Music Limited.
All Rights Reserved. International Copyright Secured.

to Coda ⊕

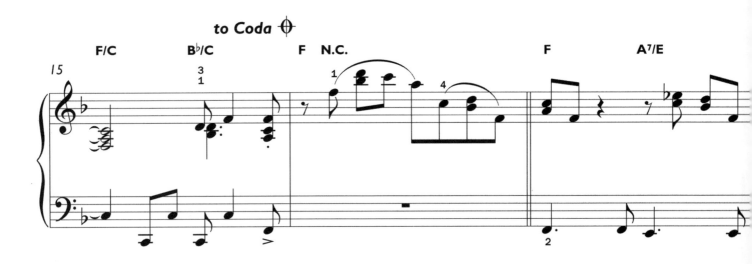

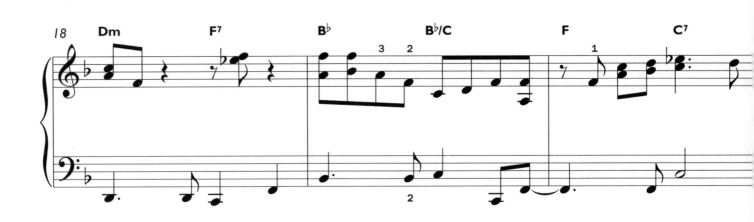

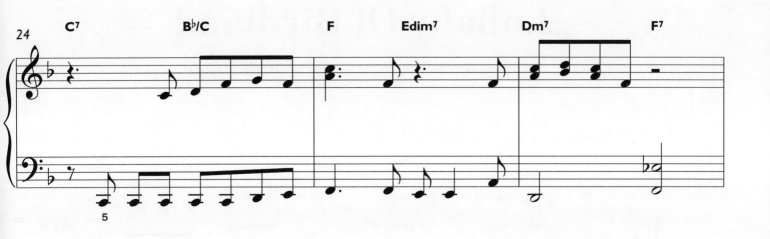

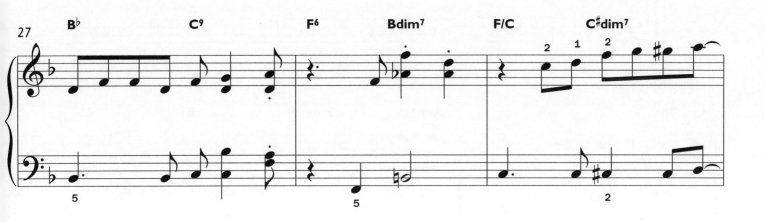

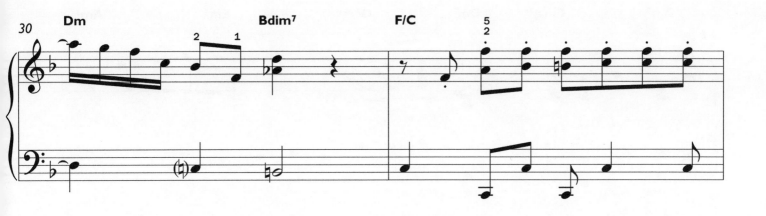

D.S. al Coda   ⊕ **Coda**
                            rit.

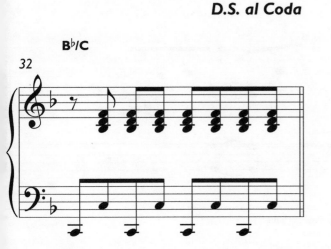

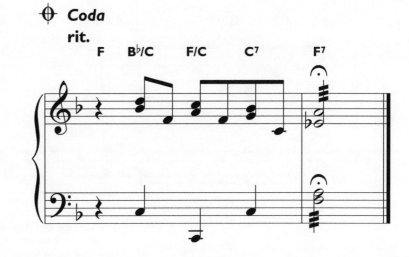

Lullaby Of Birdland

Words by George David Weiss & Music by George Shearing

© Copyright 1952, 1953 & 1954 Longitude Music Company, USA.
EMI Music Publishing (WP) Limited.
All Rights Reserved. International Copyright Secured.

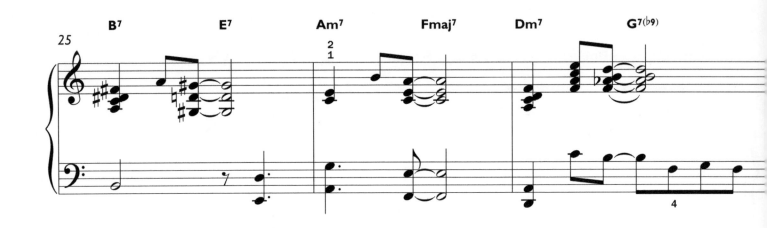

to Coda ⊕

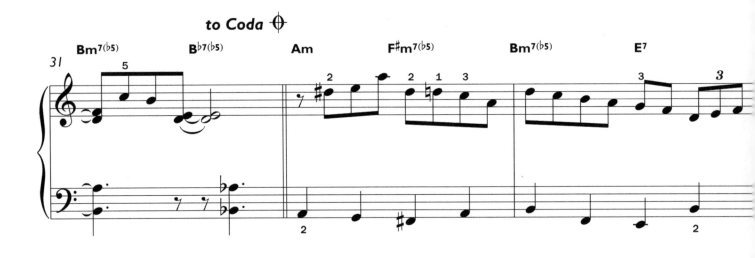

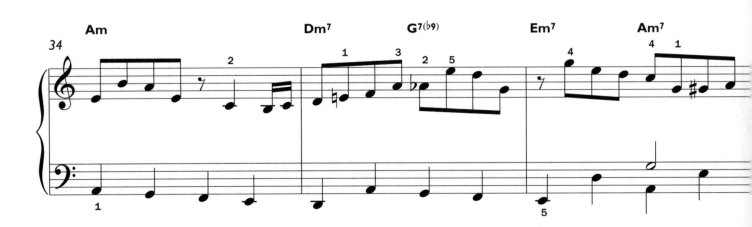

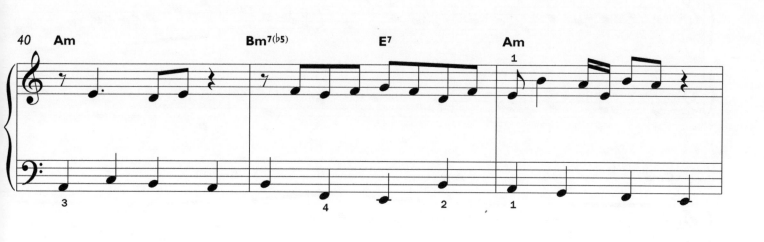

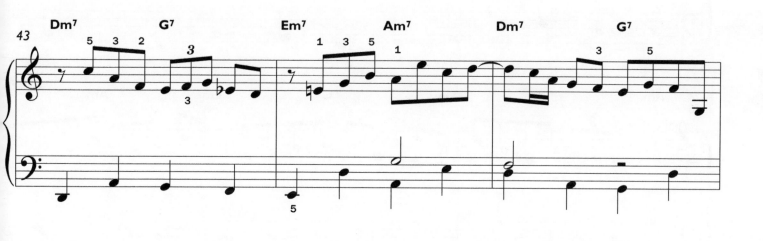

Satin Doll

Words by Johnny Mercer

Music by Duke Ellington & Billy Strayhorn

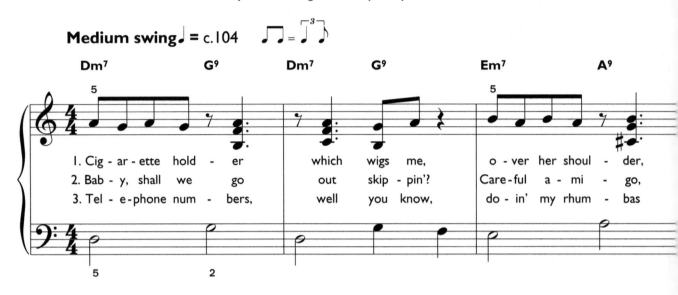

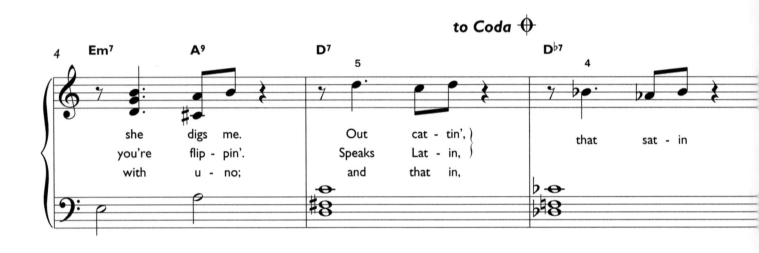

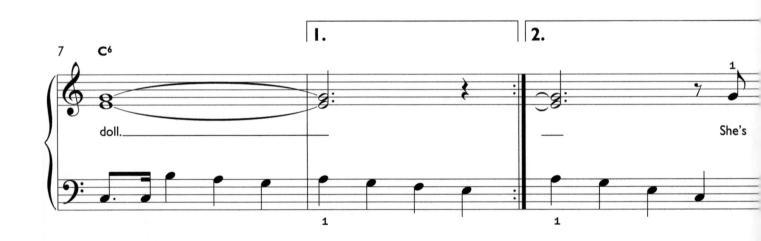

© Copyright 1953 & 1960 Tempo Music Incorporated, USA.
Campbell Connelly & Company Limited.
All Rights Reserved. International Copyright Secured.

no - bod - y's fool____ so I'm   play - ing it cool____ as can be.____

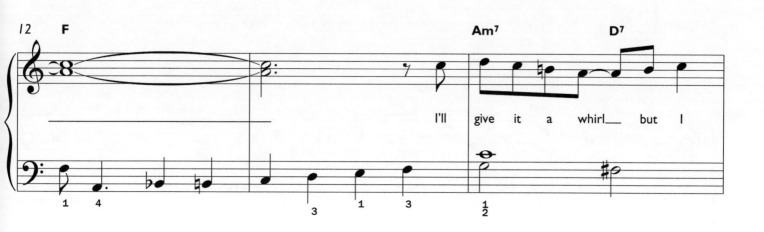

I'll give it a whirl____ but I

D.C. al Coda

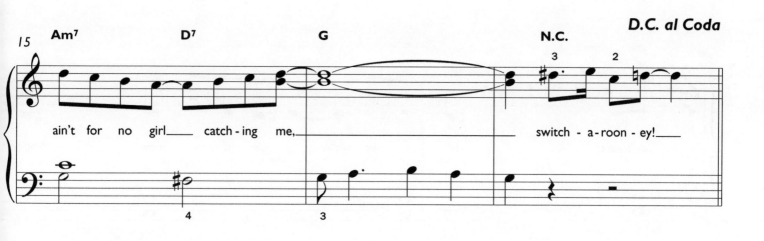

ain't for no girl____ catch - ing me,_____ switch - a - roon - ey!____

Coda

my   sat - in   doll.____

63

Well You Needn't (It's Over Now)

Music by Thelonious Monk

© Copyright 1944 (Renewed 1988) Regent Music Corporation, USA.
Blue Ribbon Music Limited.
All Rights Reserved. International Copyright Secured.

need-n't, you think you're a gas, well, you need-n't; it's

o - ver now,___ it's o - ver now. It's o - ver now,___ it's o - ver

now, you've had your fun,___ so take a bow. You

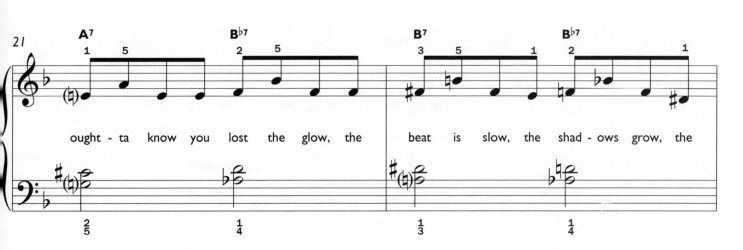

ought - ta know you lost the glow, the beat is slow, the shad - ows grow, the

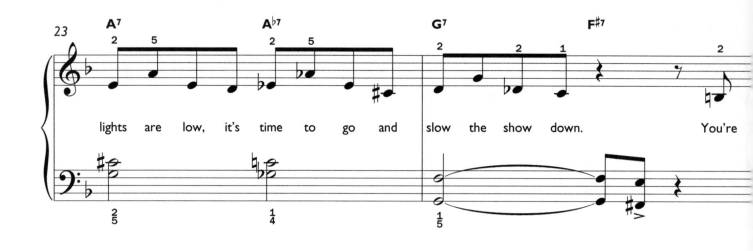

lights are low, it's time to go and slow the show down. You're

ta - kin' off weight, well, you need - n't, you're

look - in' just great, well, you need - n't, you're set - tin' the bait, well, you

need - n't; it's o - ver now,___ it's o - ver now.

(They Long To Be) Close To You

Words by Hal David & Music by Burt Bacharach

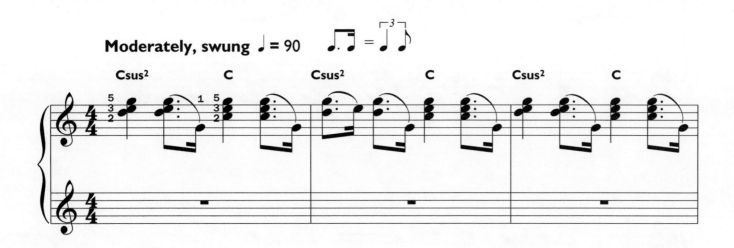

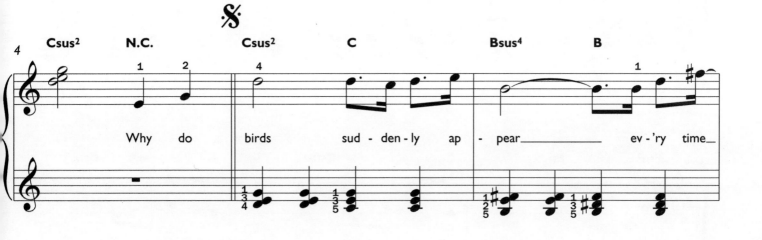

Why do birds sud - den - ly ap - pear_____ ev - 'ry time_____

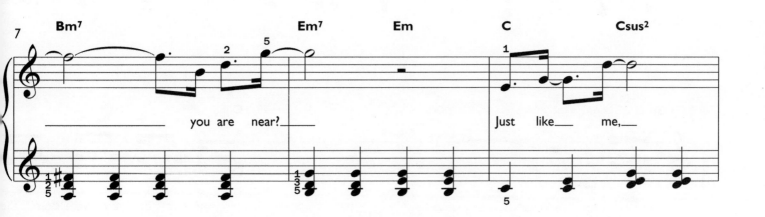

_____ you are near?____ Just like__ me,__

© Copyright 1963 Casa David Music Incorporated/New Hidden Valley Music Company, USA
Windswept Music (London) Limited (50%)/Universal/MCA Music Limited (50%).
All rights in Germany administered by Universal/MCA Music Publ. GmbH.
All Rights Reserved. International Copyright Secured.

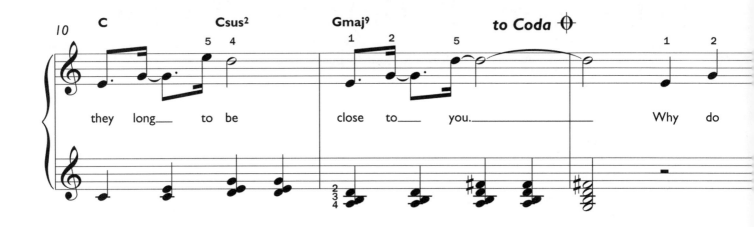

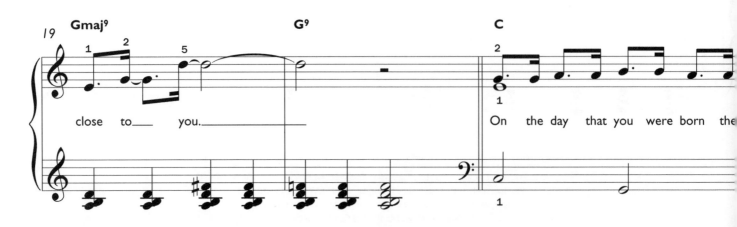

ang - els got to-geth - er and de - cid - ed to cre - ate a dream come true; so they

sprink - led moon - dust in your hair and gold - en star - light in your eyes of

D.S. al Coda **Coda**

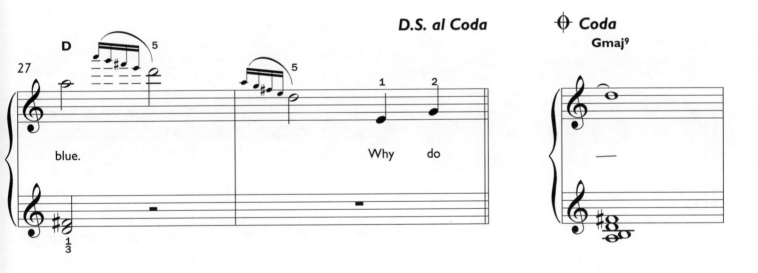

blue. Why do

Gmaj⁹

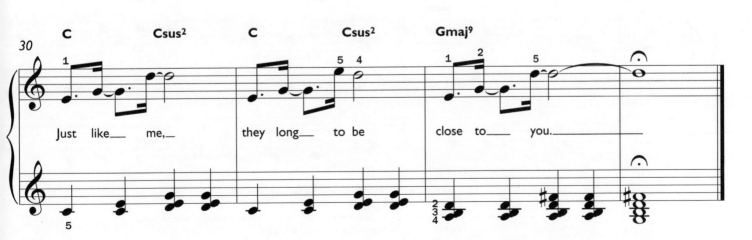

Just like___ me,___ they long___ to be close to___ you.___

69

Clocks

Words & Music by Guy Berryman, Chris Martin, Jon Buckland & Will Champion

© Copyright 2003 BMG Music Publishing Limited.
Universal Music Publishing MGB Limited.
All Rights in Germany Administered by Musik Edition Discoton GmbH (A Division of Universal Music Publishing Group).
All Rights Reserved. International Copyright Secured.

Hey Jude

Words & Music by John Lennon & Paul McCartney

Quite slowly ♩ = 75

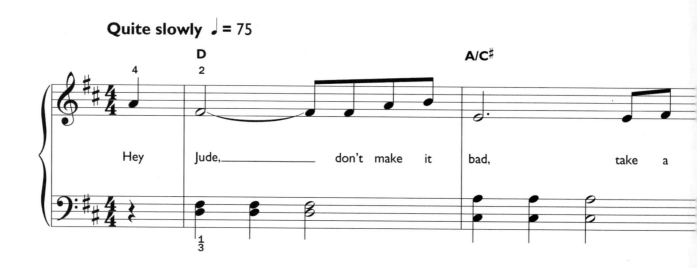

Hey   Jude,_____ don't make it   bad,   take a

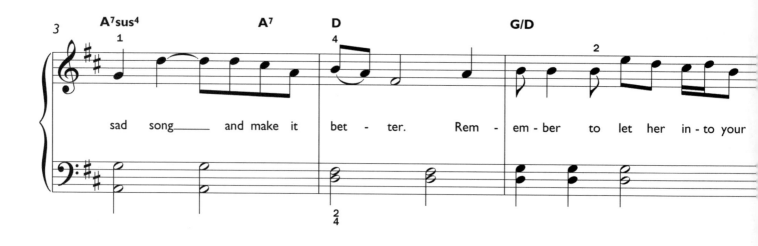

sad song____ and make it   bet - ter.   Rem - em - ber   to   let   her   in - to   your

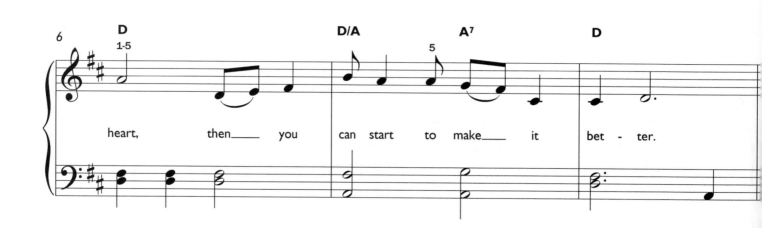

heart,   then____   you   can start   to   make____   it   bet - ter.

© Copyright 1968 Northern Songs.
All Rights Reserved. International Copyright Secured.

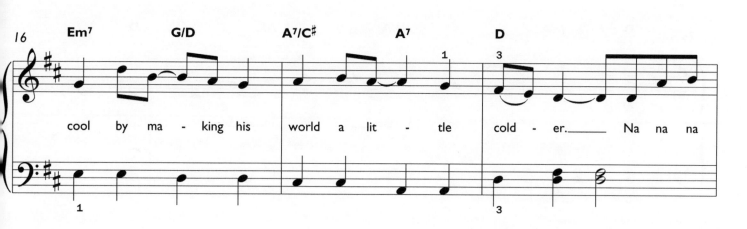

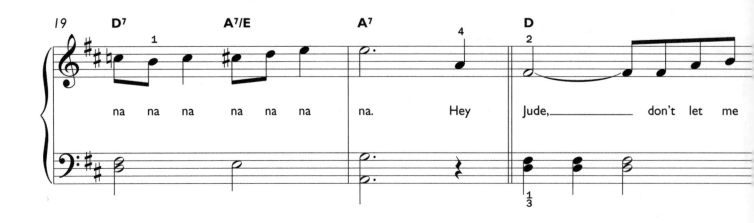

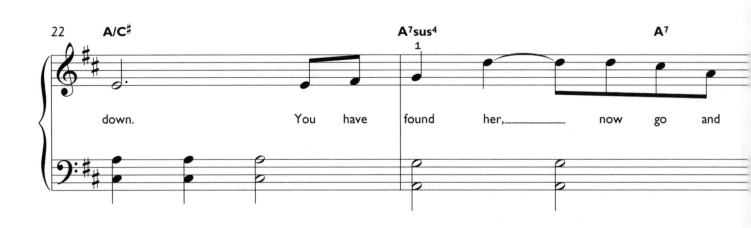

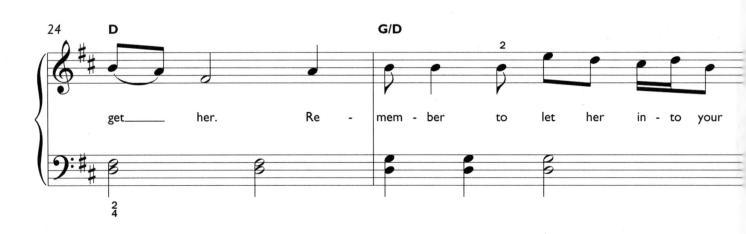

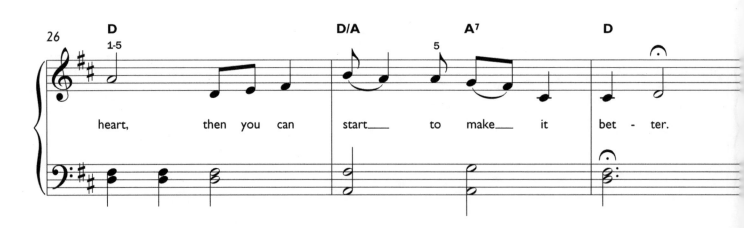

The Lady In Red

Words & Music by Chris De Burgh

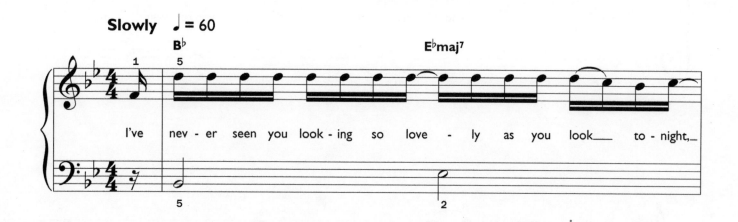

I've nev-er seen you look-ing so love-ly as you look to-night,

I've nev-er seen you shine so bright, mm, mm, mm.

I've nev-er seen so man-y men ask you if you want-ed to dance,

they're look-ing for a lit-tle ro-mance, giv-en half a

© Copyright 1986 Hornall Brothers Music Limited.
All Rights Reserved. International Copyright Secured.

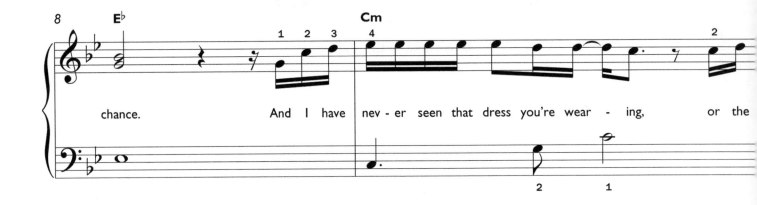

chance.   And I have nev - er seen that dress you're wear - ing,   or the

high - lights in___ your hair___ that catch__ your eyes;___   I have___ been

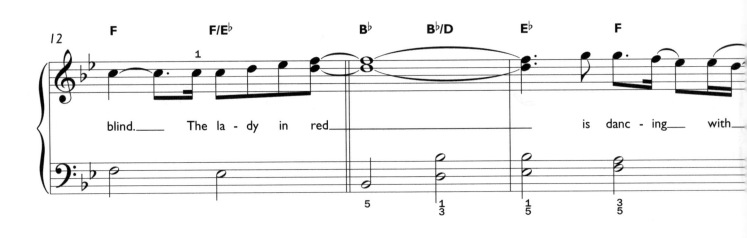

blind.___ The la - dy in red___   is danc - ing___ with

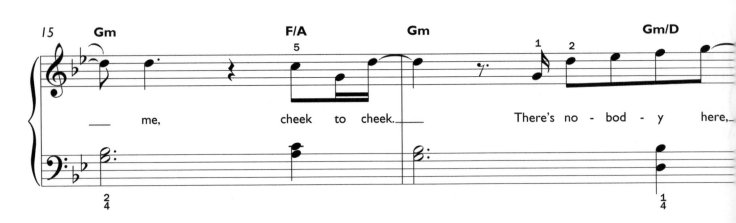

___ me,   cheek to cheek.___   There's no - bod - y here,___

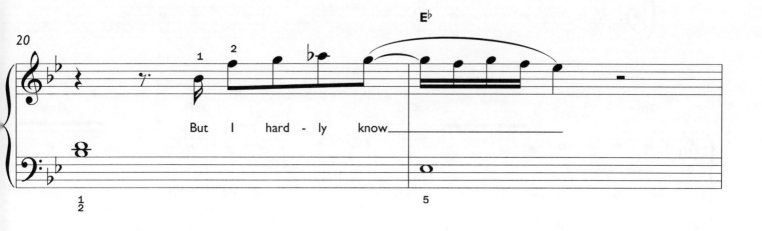

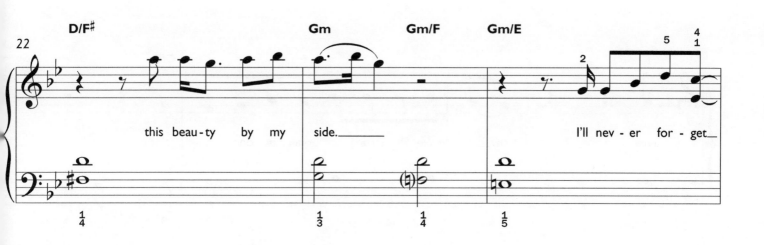

Leave Right Now

Words & Music by Francis White

I'm here_____ just like I said, though it's

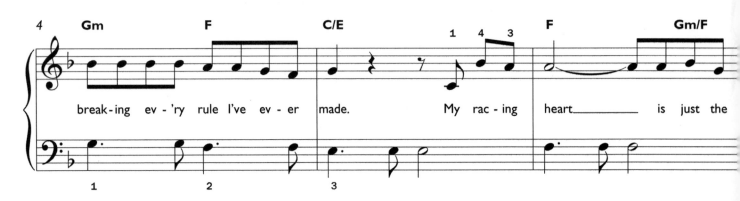

break-ing ev-'ry rule I've ev-er made. My rac-ing heart_____ is just the

same. Why___ make it strong to break it once a - gain?

And I'd love to say I do, give ev-'ry-thing to you, but I can nev-er not be

© Copyright 2003 Universal Music Publishing Limited.
All rights in Germany administered by Universal Music Publ. GmbH.
All Rights Reserved. International Copyright Secured.

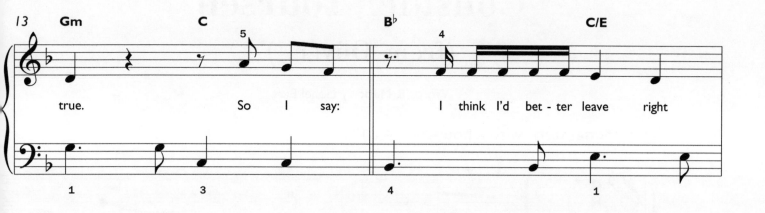

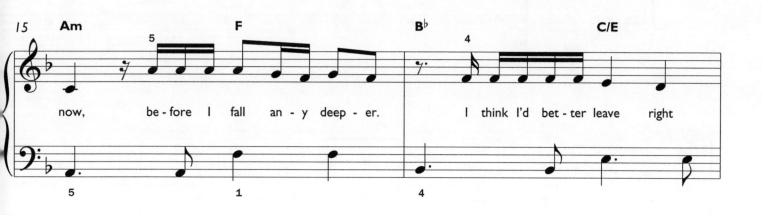

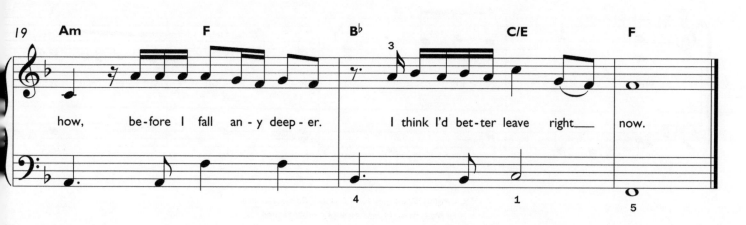

Consider Yourself

(from 'Oliver!')

Words & Music by Lionel Bart

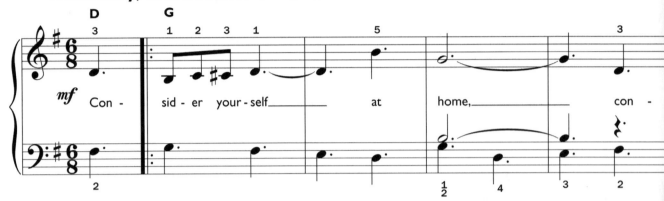

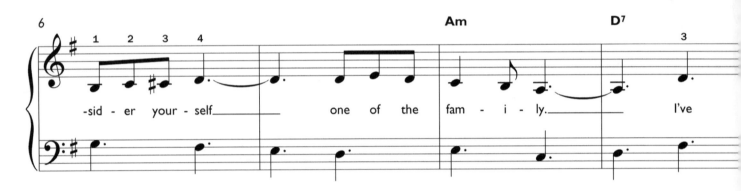

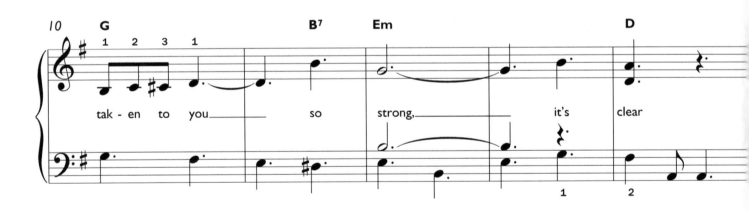

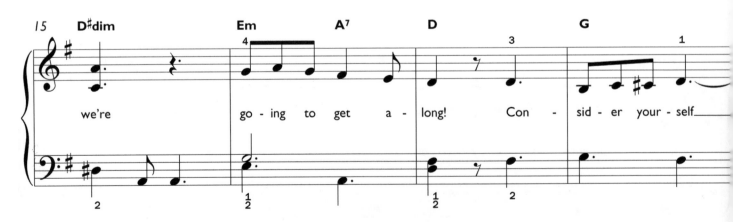

© Copyright 1959 Lakeview Music Publishing Company Limited.
All Rights Reserved. International Copyright Secured.

well in:_____ con - sid - er your-self_____ part of the

fur - ni - ture._____ There is - n't a lot_____ to

spare;_____ who cares? What - ev - er we've got we

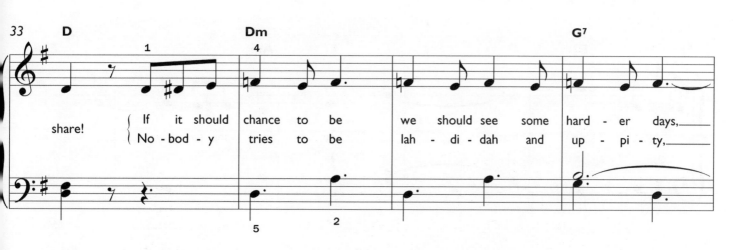

share!
{ If it should chance to be we should see some hard - er days,_____
{ No - bod - y tries to be lah - di - dah and up - pi - ty,_____

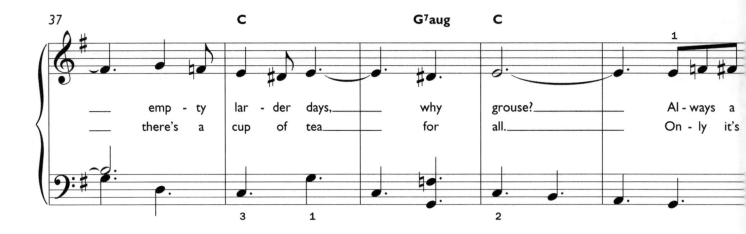

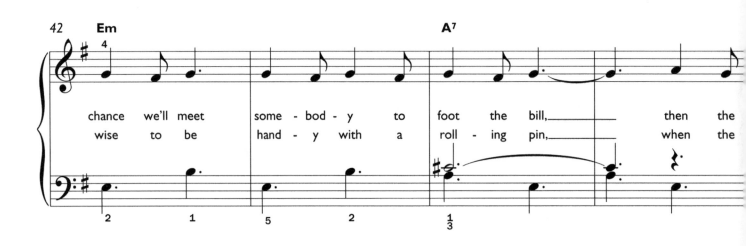

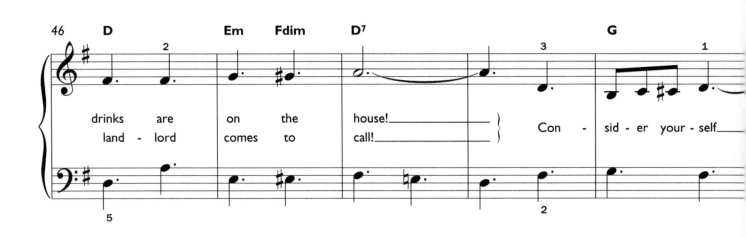

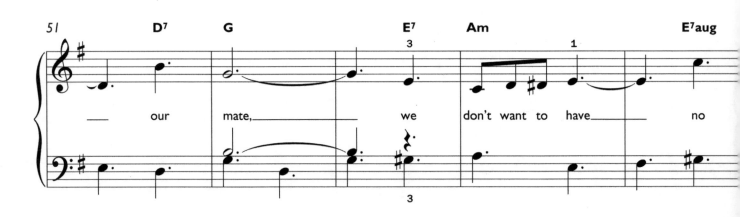

Don't Cry For Me Argentina

(from 'Evita')

Music by Andrew Lloyd Webber & Lyrics by Tim Rice

© Copyright 1976 & 1977 Evita Music Limited.
All rights in Germany administered by Universal Music Publ. GmbH.
All Rights Reserved. International Copyright Secured.

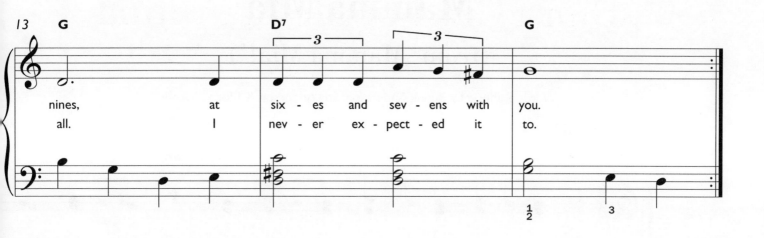

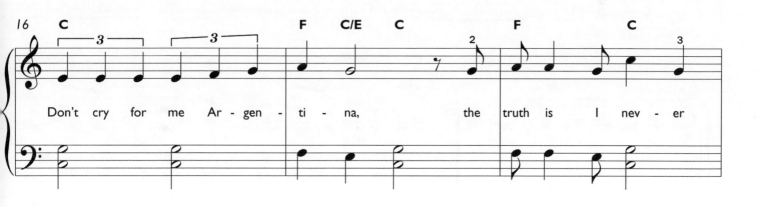

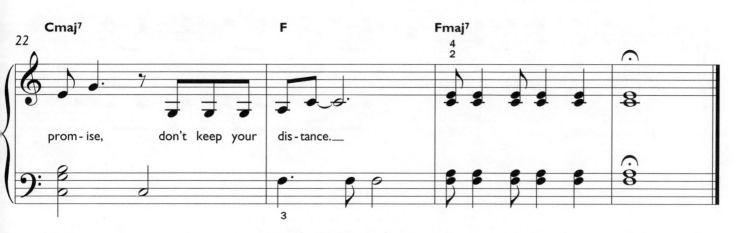

Mamma Mia

(from 'Mamma Mia!')

Words & Music by Benny Andersson, Stig Anderson & Björn Ulvaeus

Steadily ♩ = 136

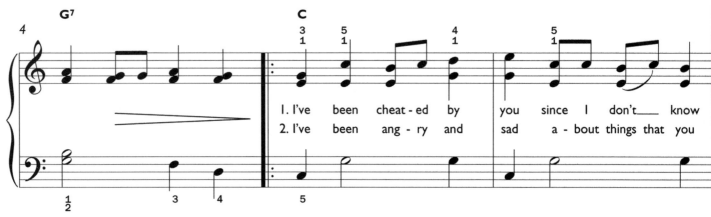

1. I've been cheat-ed by you since I don't___ know
2. I've been ang-ry and sad a-bout things that you

when. So I made up my
do. I can't count all the

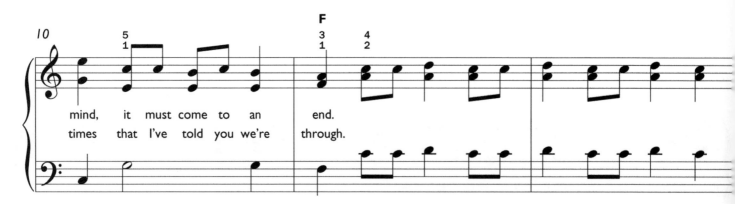

mind, it must come to an end.
times that I've told you we're through.

© Copyright 1975 Union Songs AB, Sweden.
Bocu Music Limited for Great Britain and the Republic of Ireland.
All rights in Germany administered by Universal Music Publ. GmbH.
All Rights Reserved. International Copyright Secured.

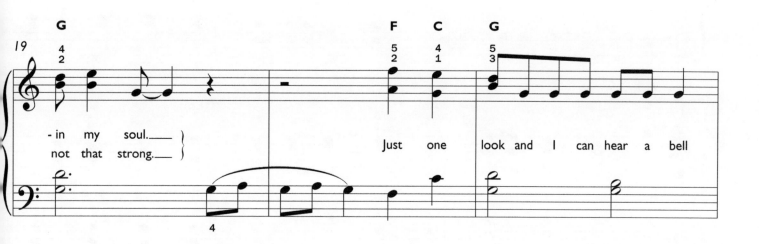

Luck Be A Lady

(from 'Guys And Dolls')

Words & Music by Frank Loesser

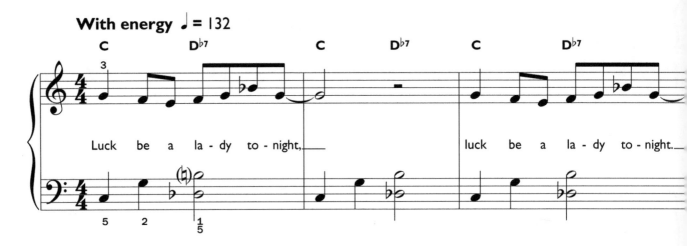

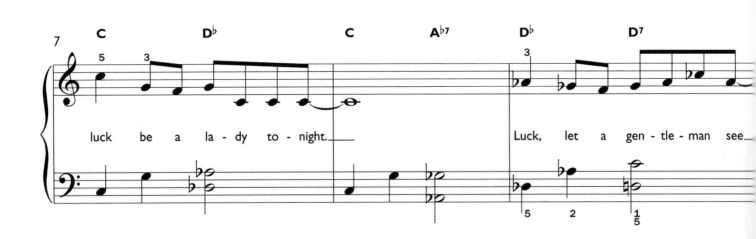

© Copyright 1950 (Renewed 1978) Frank Music Corporation, USA.
MPL Communications Limited.
All Rights Reserved. International Copyright Secured.

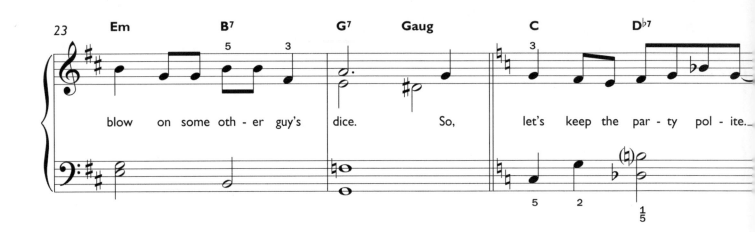

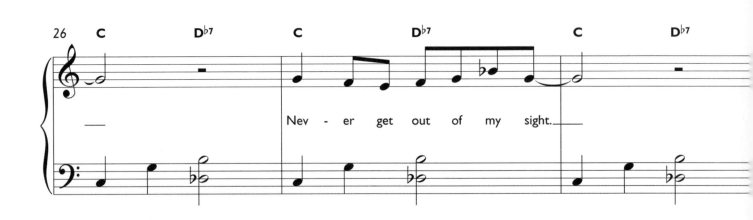

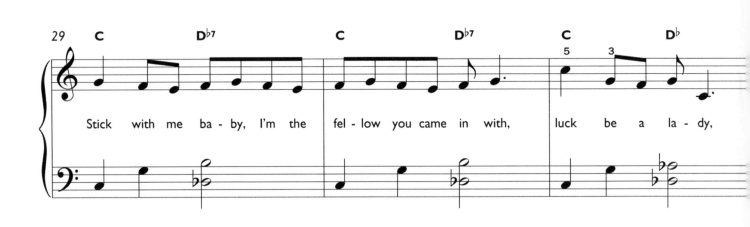

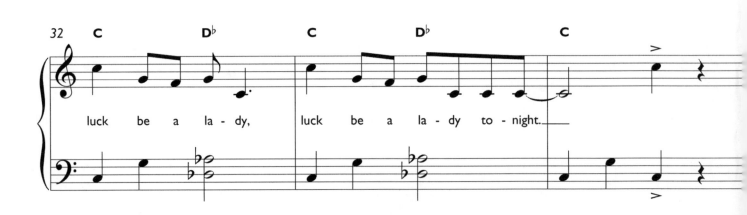

On My Own

(from 'Les Misérables')

Music by Claude-Michel Schönberg

Original Lyrics by Alain Boublil & Jean-Marc Natel

English Lyrics by Herbert Kretzmer, Trevor Nunn & John Caird

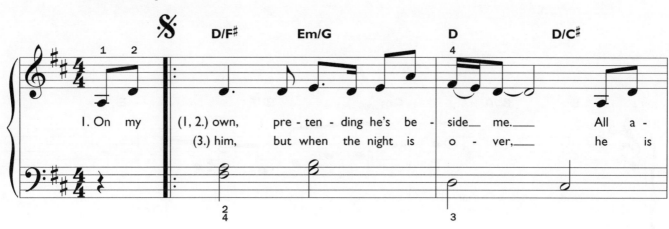

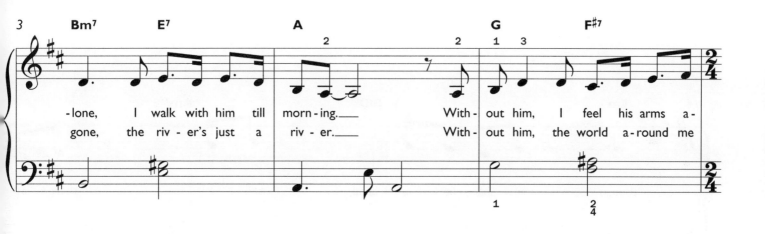

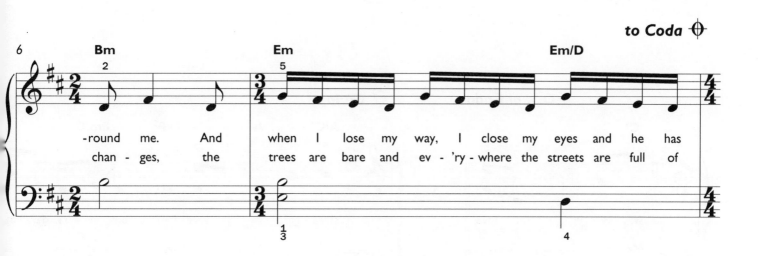

© Copyright (Music & Lyrics) 1980 Editions Musicales Alain Boublil.

English Lyrics © Copyright 1985 Alain Boublil Music Limited (ASCAP).

All Rights Reserved. International Copyright Secured.

found me.___ 2. On my found me. And I know it's on-ly in my

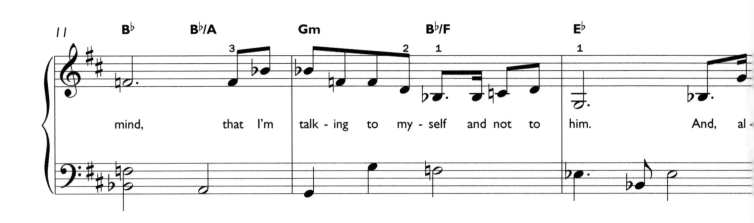

mind, that I'm talk-ing to my-self and not to him. And, al-

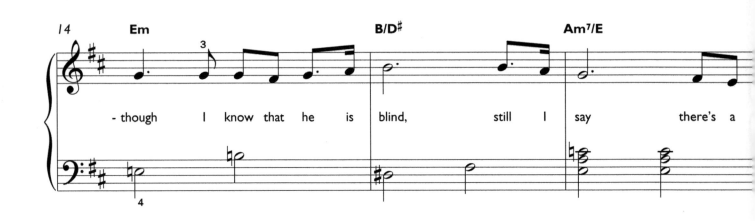

-though I know that he is blind, still I say there's a

D.S. al Coda

⊕ **Coda**

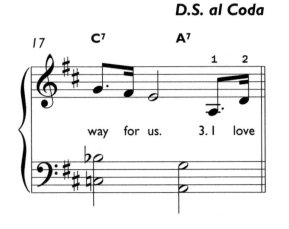

way for us. 3. I love

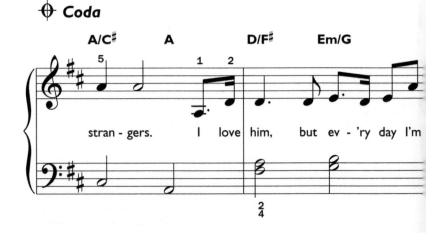

stran-gers. I love him, but ev-'ry day I'm

94

learn - ing._____ All my life, I've on - ly been pre -

- tend - ing._____ With - out me, his world will go on turn - ing. The

world is full of hap - pi - ness that I have nev - er known. I love

him, I love him. I love him, but on - ly on my own.

3 4 5 6 7 8 9
12/09 (172579)

Bringing you the words and the music

All the latest music in print... rock & pop plus jazz, blues, countr classical and the best in West End show scores.

- Books to match your favourite CDs.

- Book-and-CD titles with high quality backing tracks for you to play along to. Now you can play guitar or piano with y favourite artist... or simply sing along!

- Audition songbooks with CD backing tracks for both male and female singe for all those with stars in their eyes.

- Can't read music? No problem, you ca still play all the hits with our wide rang chord songbooks.

- Check out our range of instrumental tutorial titles, taking you from novice to expert in no time at all!

- Musical show scores include *The Phar Of The Opera*, *Les Misérables*, *Mamma Mia* and many more hit productions.

- DVD master classes featuring the techniques of top artists.

Visit your local music shop or, in case of difficulty, contact the Marketing Department, Music Sales Limited, Newmarket Road, Bury St Edmunds, Suffolk, IP33 3YB, UK
marketing@musicsales.co.uk